SESAME STREET

Let's Share

MY FIRST MANNERS

Written by Constance Allen
Illustrated by Maggie Swanson

Published by Louis Weber, C.E.O., Publications International, Ltd., 7373 North Cicero Avenue, Lincolnwood, Illinois 60712
Ground Floor, 59 Gloucester Place, London W1U 8JJ

Customer Service: 1-800-595-8484 or customer_service@pilbooks.com

www.pilbooks.com

p i kids is a registered trademark of Publications International, Ltd.

8 7 6 5 4 3 2 1

ISBN-13: 978-1-4127-8387-3   ISBN-10: 1-4127-8387-9

 publications international, ltd.

What should the monster do?

Give you a hint: It rhymes with
"Try to be **fair**!"

Share! Especially when you've got two!

What should the monster do?

Give you a hint: It rhymes with
"Give up your **chair**!"

Share! It's the polite thing to do!

What should the monster do?

Give you a hint: It rhymes with
"He has an extra **pear**."

Share! It's the nice thing to do!

What should the monster do?

Give you a hint: It rhymes with
"She's got a **spare**."

Share! Games are more fun
when they're played by two!

What should the monster do?

Give you a hint: It rhymes with
"Wet **hair**!"

Share! It's the thoughtful thing to do!

What should the monster do?

What do the monsters do?

You guessed it! **Share**!